MONEY MAP™

CROWN FINANCIAL MINISTRIES

JOURNEY TO FINANCIAL FREEDOM MANUAL

LARRY BURKETT

CROWN FINANCIAL MINISTRIE

True Financial Freedom

CROWN.ORG

Verses identified as (KJV) are taken from the King James Version.

Verses identified as (NIV) are taken from the *Holy Bible: New International Version,* © 1973, 1978, 1984 by the International Bible Society. Used by permission of Zondervan Bible Publishers.

Verses identified as (Amplified) are taken from the *Amplified New Testament,* © 1954, 1958, 1987 by The Lockman Foundation. Used by permission.

Verses identified as (TLB) are taken from *The Living Bible,* © 1971 by Tyndale House Publishers, Wheaton, IL. Used by permission.

All other verses are from the *New American Standard Bible,*® © 1960, 1962, 1963, 1968, 1971, 1972, 1973, 1975, 1977 by The Lockman Foundation, or the *New American Standard Bible*® (updated edition), copyright 1960, 1962, 1963, 1968, 1971, 1972, 1973, 1975, 1977, 1995 by The Lockman Foundation. Used by permission.

No part of this book may be reproduced without written permission, except for brief quotations in books and critical reviews and for copying the blank forms for the purchaser's use.

ISBN 1-56427-106-4

© 2003, 2005 by Crown Financial Ministries
PO Box 100, Gainesville GA 30503-0100
All rights reserved. Printed in the USA.

WELCOME

Journey to Financial Freedom is designed to be a helpful tool in the ministry of Money Map coaching. It contains forms for developing spending plans and assignments based on important scriptural financial principles that will impact future financial decisions.

USE OF THIS MANUAL

This manual is divided into five sessions. Each session begins with a suggested outline for the coach to follow. Since all financial situations are different, the Money Map Coach determines how rapidly progress is made through the manual and what will be covered in each session. In some cases, additional assignments would prove helpful based on the recommendation of the Money Map Coach. It is our prayer that this manual and coaching experience will be a blessing to all those who participate.

The *Journey to Financial Freedom* Quick Guide
For the Money Map Coach

1. What is the *Journey to Financial Freedom Manual?*

- A concise manual that includes the forms, homework assignments, and information sheets for Money Map Coaches to use as they coach. This manual will ultimately belong to the coaching participant. This manual is not intended for personal study without the guidance of a Money Map Coach.

- The manual is divided into five sessions. Each session begins with a suggested outline. You, as the coach, determine what is actually covered in each session, in what sequence the homework is given, and how many sessions you will have.

- If deemed necessary, the manual can be used with other forms of study, such as the *Family Financial Workbook* or the *How to Manage Your Money Workbook.*

2. How do I use the *Journey to Financial Freedom Manual?*

- The key to the proper use of this manual is FLEXIBILITY! Not everyone will come to you with the same needs and financial/scriptural knowledge.

- Determine the needs of the coaching participant and structure the assignments to meet those needs.

3. How do I use the *Crown Money Map*™?

- We strongly encourage you to use the Crown Money Map in the first coaching session with each coaching participant and to give each participating person/couple a copy of the Money Map. Many people have no idea that there are financial goals beyond simply paying each month's bills. As you show them the destinations on the Money Map, you can give them hope and a vision for achieving long-term goals after their immediate financial dilemma is resolved.

CONTENTS

JOURNEY TO FINANCIAL FREEDOM

SESSION ONE OUTLINE

Initial Meeting (1½ to 2 hours)

❑ 1. **Open in prayer**

❑ 2. **Personal Information Sheet**

❑ 3. **A Commitment to Coaching**

❑ 4. **Overview of Money Map**

❑ 5. **Forms—overview and explanation**
- ❑ List of Debts
- ❑ Financial Statement
- ❑ Monthly Income and Expenses

❑ 6. **Diagnosis of Financial Health**
- ❑ Is the use of Financial Hope a possibility? (see page 69)
- ❑ Spending decisions

❑ 7. **Goals**
- ❑ Optimistic view of debt reduction, savings, investing, personal goals, spiritual goals

❑ 8. **Action Steps**
- ❑ 30-Day Diary (spreadsheet and or pocket notebook)
- ❑ Balance budget using a new Monthly Income and Expense
- ❑ Fill out the Quit Claim deed
- ❑ Additional recommendations
- ❑ Homework assignment #1
- ❑ Set date for next meeting

❑ 9. **Close in prayer**

Personal Information Sheet

1. How did you hear about this coaching ministry? _____

    _____

    _____

2. Please list the following church-related information.

    a. Do you presently attend church? _____

    b. If so, where do you attend? _____

    c. What is your pastor's name? _____

3. How many children do you have living at home and what are their ages?

    _____

    _____

4. Other information

    Date_____

    Name_____

    Address _____

    City _____State _____Zip Code _____

    Telephone: Home (____) _____   Office (____) _____

    E-mail_____   Cell phone (____) _____

    Pager_____

    Occupation _____

    Spouse _____

    Family birthdays

    Name _____   Birthday _____

    Name _____   Birthday _____

    Name _____   Birthday _____

    Name _____   Birthday _____

A COMMITMENT TO COACHING

As a Christian, I believe God's Word to be the guidebook for living. It is my desire to obey the Lord in every aspect of life. Today, I agree to submit to God's Word and the biblical instruction given in Proverbs 19:20-21, *"Listen to counsel and accept discipline, that you may be wise the rest of your days. Many plans are in a man's heart, but the counsel of the Lord will stand."*

I do commit to the following as God gives me ability.

1. Having no more debt.

2. Studying the Bible as assigned and as God leads.

3. Faithfully keeping appointments with my coach.

4. Placing God first and honoring Him by living on a budget.

I will do my best to keep focused on the agreed-on goals, so that beginning today God will be pleased with my life. I am trusting in the promise given in Proverbs 3:4-5, *"Trust in the Lord with all your heart and do not lean on your own understanding. In all your ways acknowledge Him, and He will make your paths straight."*

Signed: Date:

_____   _____

_____   _____

As a coach:

I do commit to the following as God gives me ability.

1. Faithfully keeping my appointments with you.

2. Presenting the biblical principles of handling money and explaining how they apply to your situation.

3. Faithfully praying for you.

Signed: Date:

_____   _____

_____   _____

LIST OF DEBTS

as of _____

To Whom Owed	Contact Name Phone Number	Pay Off	Payments Left	Monthly Payment	Date Due	Interest Rate

Crown Financial Ministries 2/03

FINANCIAL STATEMENT

as of _____

ASSETS
   Liquid Assets[1]

   _____ $ _____

LIABILITIES[4]

_____ $ _____

   Total Liquid Assets $ _____

TOTAL LIABILITIES $ _____

   Invested Assets[2]

   _____ $ _____

NET WORTH $ _____
(Assets-Liabilities)

   Total Invested $ _____

   Use Assets[3]

   _____ $ _____

**TOTAL LIABILITIES
AND NET WORTH** $ _____

   Total Use Assets $ _____

   TOTAL ASSETS $ _____

[1] Cash, Savings Accounts, Checking Accounts
[2] IRAs, TSAs, 401(K)s, Investment, Real Estate, CDs, Antiques presented at fair market value.
[3] Residence, Autos, Personal Belongings presented at fair market value.
[4] Outstanding Real Estate Loans, Credit Cards, Auto Loans, Personal Loans.

Crown Financial Ministries 2/03

MONTHLY INCOME AND EXPENSES

GROSS INCOME PER MONTH _____

    Salary _____

    Interest _____

    Dividends _____

    Other (_____) _____

    Other (_____) _____

LESS:

  1. Tithe _____

  2. Tax (Est. - Incl. Fed., State, FICA) _____

    NET SPENDABLE INCOME _____

  3. Housing _____

    Mortgage (rent) _____

    Insurance _____

    Taxes _____

    Electricity _____

    Gas _____

    Water _____

    Sanitation _____

    Telephone _____

    Maintenance _____

    Other (_____) _____

    Other (_____) _____

  4. Food _____

  5. Automobile(s) _____

    Payments _____

    Gas and Oil _____

    Insurance _____

    License/Taxes _____

    Maint./Repair/Replace _____

  6. Insurance _____

    Life _____

    Medical _____

    Other (_____) _____

  7. Debts _____

    Credit Card _____

    Loans and Notes _____

    Other (_____) _____

    Other (_____) _____

8. Enter./Recreation _____

    Eating Out _____

    Baby Sitters _____

    Activities/Trips _____

    Vacation _____

    Other (_____) _____

    Other (_____) _____

9. Clothing _____

10. Savings _____

11. Medical Expenses _____

    Doctor _____

    Dentist _____

    Credit Card _____

    Other (_____) _____

12. Miscellaneous _____

    Toiletry, cosmetics _____

    Beauty, barber _____

    Laundry, cleaning _____

    Allowances, lunches _____

    Subscriptions _____

    Gifts (incl. Christmas) _____

    Cash _____

    Cable/Internet _____

    Other (_____) _____

    Other (_____) _____

13. Investments _____

14. School/Child Care _____

    Tuition _____

    Materials _____

    Transportation _____

    Day Care _____

    Other (_____) _____

TOTAL EXPENSES _____

INCOME VERSUS EXPENSES

  Net Spendable Income _____

  Less Expenses _____

15. Unallocated Surplus Income[1]

[1] This category is used when surplus income is received. This would be kept in the checking account to be used within a few weeks; otherwise, it should be transferred to an allocated category.

Crown Financial Ministries 2/03

Financial Goals for the _____ family

Category	Specific Goal	Time Frame	Goal Successfully Met
Savings	We will save $5 a week to place toward a lamp replacement	6 weeks	1-June
Debt Retirement	We will reduce our consumer debt by $100 per month until it is gone	Monthly	1/31, 2/29, 3/31, 4/31
Offering	We will give an additional $25 per month to the church for missionary work	Ongoing as God provides	1/31, 2/29,

Personal and Spiritual Goals for the _____ family

Category	Specific Goal	Time Frame	Goal Successfully Met
Personal Goals			
Spiritual Goals			

Crown Financial Ministries 2/03

ACTION STEPS

30-Day Diary

Category	INCOME	TITHE/GIVING	TAXES	HOUSING	FOOD	TRANSPORTATION	INSURANCE
BUDGETED AMOUNT	$	$	$	$	$	$	$
Date							
1							
2							
3							
4							
5							
6							
7							
8							
9							
10							
11							
12							
13							
14							
15							
This month SUBTOTAL	$	$	$	$	$	$	$
16							
17							
18							
19							
20							
21							
22							
23							
24							
25							
26							
27							
28							
29							
30							
31							
This month TOTAL	$	$	$	$	$	$	$
This month SURPLUS/DEFICIT	$	$	$	$	$	$	$
Year to Date BUDGET	$	$	$	$	$	$	$
Year to Date TOTAL	$	$	$	$	$	$	$
Year to Date SURPLUS/DEFICIT	$	$	$	$	$	$	$

BUDGET SUMMARY

This Month		Previous Month/Year to Date		Year to Date
Total Income $ _____		Total Income $ _____		Total Income $ _____
Minus Total Expenses $ _____	**+**	Minus Total Expenses $ _____	**=**	Minus Total Expenses $ _____
Equals Surplus/Deficit $ _____		Equals Surplus/Deficit $ _____		Equals Surplus/Deficit $ _____

30-Day Diary

Category	DEBTS	ENT./REC.	CLOTHING	SAVINGS	MEDICAL	MISCELLANEOUS	INVESTMENTS	SCHOOL/DAYCARE
BUDGETED AMOUNT	$	$	$	$	$	$	$	$
Date								
1								
2								
3								
4								
5								
6								
7								
8								
9								
10								
11								
12								
13								
14								
15								
This month SUBTOTAL	$	$	$	$	$	$	$	$
16								
17								
18								
19								
20								
21								
22								
23								
24								
25								
26								
27								
28								
29								
30								
31								
This month TOTAL	$	$	$	$	$	$	$	$
This month SURPLUS/DEFICIT	$	$	$	$	$	$	$	$
Year to Date BUDGET	$	$	$	$	$	$	$	$
Year to Date TOTAL	$	$	$	$	$	$	$	$
Year to Date SURPLUS/DEFICIT	$	$	$	$	$	$	$	$

Quit Claim Deed

This Quit Claim Deed, Made the _____ day of _____

From: _____

To: The Lord

I (we) hereby transfer to the Lord the ownership of the following possessions:

Witnesses who hold me (us)
accountable in the recognition
of the Lord's ownership:

_____

_____

Stewards of the possessions
above:

_____

_____

This instrument is not a binding legal document and cannot be used to transfer property.

COACHING SESSION ONE

God's Part and Our Part

Key Scripture

"The earth is the Lord's, and all it contains" (Psalm 24:1).

QUESTIONS TO ANSWER

1. **Read *Deuteronomy 10:14* and *Psalm 24:1*.**
   What do these passages teach about the ownership of your possessions?

   Prayerfully evaluate your attitude of ownership toward your possessions. Do you consistently recognize the true owner of those possessions? Write a practical idea that will help you recognize God's ownership.

2. **Read *1 Chronicles 29:11-12* and *Psalm 135:6*.**
   What do these verses say about God and His control?

   Do you normally recognize the Lord's control of all events? If not, how can you become more consistent in recognizing His control?

3. **Read *Genesis 45:4-8* and *Romans 8:28*.**
   Why is it important to realize that God is in control and uses even difficult circumstances for good in the life of a godly person?

Describe a difficult circumstance you have experienced and how the Lord ultimately used it for good in your life.

4. **Read *Psalm 34:9-10; Matthew 6:31-33*; and *Philippians 4:19*.**
   What has the Lord promised concerning meeting your needs?

   How does this apply to you today?

5. **Read *1 Corinthians 4:2*.**
   The key to understanding God's will in finances is the proper understanding of our role. What does this verse say is our requirement as stewards? What is the definition of a steward?

6. **Read *Luke 16:10*.**
   Describe the principle found in this verse.

   How does this apply in your situation?

7. **Read *Luke 16:12*.**
   Are we required to be faithful with other people's possessions? What happens if we are not?

NOTES TO READ

It may surprise you to learn just how much the Bible says about finances. There are hundreds of verses about how to handle money and possessions. In fact, Jesus Christ said more about money than almost any other subject.

The Lord talked so much about money because he knew that money would be a struggle for many of us. Because He loves us, God gave us His roadmap for handling money. Some of the topics the Bible covers are how to earn, spend, save, get out of debt, give, invest, budget, and train children to manage money.

The most important point to understand is the part God plays in our finances.

THE LORD OWNS ALL OUR POSSESSIONS

"Behold, to the Lord your God belong…the earth and all that is in it" (Deuteronomy 10:14). *"The earth is the Lord's, and all it contains"* (Psalm 24:1). The Bible reveals that the Lord is the Creator of all things, *"In the beginning God created the heavens and the earth"* (Genesis 1:1). He has never transferred the ownership of His creation to people. When we acknowledge God's ownership, every spending decision becomes a spiritual decision. No longer do we ask, "Lord, what do You want me to do with *my* money?" The question is restated, "Lord, what do You want me to do with *Your* money?"

Consistently recognizing God's ownership is difficult. It is easy to believe intellectually that God owns all you have and yet still live as if this were not true.

THE LORD IS IN CONTROL

Besides being Owner, God is ultimately in control of every event that occurs on the earth. *"We adore you as being in control of everything"* (1 Chronicles 29:11, TLB). *"Whatever the Lord pleases, He does, in heaven and in earth"* (Psalm 135:6).

It is important for the child of God to realize that His heavenly Father uses even seemingly devastating circumstances for ultimate good in the lives of the godly. *"We know that God causes all things to work togeth-*

[God is the] Creator, the Almighty, eternal, all-knowing, all-powerful, omnipresent, awesome, Lord of lords and King of kings.

er for good to those who love God, to those who are called according to His purpose" (Romans 8:28).

THE LORD PROVIDES

The Lord promises to provide our needs. *"Seek first His kingdom and His righteousness, and all these things* [food and clothing] *shall be added to you"* (Matthew 6:33). The same Lord who fed 5,000 with only five loaves and two fish has promised to provide our needs.

God is both predictable and unpredictable. He is absolutely predictable in His faithfulness to provide for our needs. What we cannot predict is *how* the Lord will provide. He uses various, and often surprising, means of meeting our needs: an increase in income or a gift. He may provide an opportunity to stretch our limited resources through money-saving purchases. Regardless of how He chooses to provide for our needs, He is completely reliable.

GET TO KNOW GOD

God, as He is revealed in Scripture, is much different than the way people commonly imagine Him to be. Our tendency is to shrink God and fit Him into a mold with human abilities and limitations. Our failure to recognize God's part is due to the fact that we do not understand the greatness of God, *"Who stretched out the heavens and laid the foundations of the earth"* (Isaiah 51:13). How do we capture the true perspective of God? Primarily through studying what the Bible tells us about Him.

Carefully review some of His names and attributes: Creator, the Almighty, eternal, all-knowing, all-powerful, omnipresent, awesome, Lord of lords, and King of kings. The Lord's power and ability is incomprehensible. Astronomers estimate that there are more than 100 billion galaxies in the universe, each containing billions of stars. The enormity of the universe is mind boggling. *"Lift up your eyes on high and see who has created these stars, the One who leads forth their host by number, He calls them all by name; because of the greatness of His might and the strength of His power, not one of them is missing"* (Isaiah 40:26).

God is intimately involved with each of us as individuals. His Word reveals, *"You are familiar with all my ways. Before a word is on my tongue You know it completely, O Lord . . . All the days ordained for me were written in your book before one of them came to be"* (Psalm 139:3-4,16, NIV). The Lord is so involved in our lives that He reassures us: *"The very hairs of your head are all numbered"* (Matthew 10:30). Our heavenly Father is the One who knows us the best and loves us the most.

WE ARE STEWARDS

We are stewards, or managers, of the possessions the Lord has entrusted to us, and our only responsibility is to be faithful. *"Moreover, it is required in stewards, that a man be found faithful"* (1 Corinthians 4:2, KJV). Before we can be faithful, we must know what we are required to do. Just as the purchaser of a complicated piece of machinery studies the manufacturer's manual to learn how to operate it, we need to examine the Creator's handbook—the Bible—to determine how He wants us to handle His possessions.

Two elements of our responsibility to be faithful are important to understand.

1. To be faithful with what we are given

The Lord requires us to be faithful, regardless of how much He has entrusted to us. The parable of the talents illustrates this. *"It is just like a man about to go on a journey, who called his own slaves and entrusted his possessions to them. To one he gave five talents, to another, two, and to another, one, each according to his own ability"* (Matthew 25:14-15).

When the master returned, he held each slave accountable for faithfully managing his possessions. Read the master's commendation of the faithful slave who received the five talents: *"Well done, good and faithful slave. You were faithful with a few things, I will put you in charge of many things; enter into the joy of your master"* (Matthew 25:21). Interestingly, the slave who had been given two talents received the identical reward as the slave who had been given the five talents (see Matthew 25:23). The Lord rewards faithfulness, regardless of the amount over which we are responsible.

We are required to be faithful whether we are given much or little. As someone once said, "It's not what I would do if $1 million were my lot; it's what I am doing with the $10 I've got."

2. To be faithful in every area

God requires us to be faithful in handling 100 percent of our money, not just 10 percent. Most Christians have been taught only how to handle 10 percent of their income—the area of giving. And although this area is crucial, by default we have allowed the body of Christ to learn how

We are required to be faithful whether we are given much or little.

to handle the other 90 percent from the world's perspective, not from our Lord's perspective.

Ignorance of scriptural financial principles frequently causes money problems. Many Christians have wrong attitudes toward possessions, and this causes them to make incorrect financial decisions and suffer painful consequences.

PRINCIPLES OF FAITHFULNESS

1. Faithfulness with our possessions

"There was a rich man who had a manager [steward], *and this manager was reported to him as squandering his possessions. And he called him and said to him, 'What is this I hear about you? Give an account of your management* [stewardship], *for you can no longer be manager* [steward]' "* (Luke 16:1,2).

There are two principles from this passage that are applicable to us. First of all, when we waste our possessions it becomes public knowledge and creates a poor testimony (*"this manager was reported to him as squandering his possessions"*). Secondly, the Lord will remove us as stewards if we squander what He has given us.

2. Faithfulness in little things

"He who is faithful in a very little thing is faithful also in much; and he who is unrighteous in a very little thing is unrighteous also in much" (Luke 16:10).

How do you know if your son is going to take good care of his first car? Observe how he cared for his bicycle. How do you know if a salesperson will do a competent job of serving a large client? Evaluate how he or she served a small client. If we have the character to be faithful with small things, the Lord knows He can trust us with greater responsibilities. Hudson Taylor said, "Small things are small things, but faithfulness with a small thing is a big thing."

3. Faithfulness with another's possessions

Faithfulness with another's possessions will, in some measure, determine how much you are given. *"If you have not been faithful in the use of that which is another's, who will give you that which is your own?"* (Luke 16:12).

This is a principle that is often overlooked. Are you faithful with others' possessions? Are you careless with your employer's office supplies? When someone allows you to use something, are you careful to return it in good shape? Some people have not been entrusted with more, because they have been unfaithful with the possessions of others.

Please prayerfully review these principles of faithfulness.

"If you have not been faithful in the use of that which is another's, who will give you that which is your own?" (Luke 16:12).

SESSION TWO OUTLINE

Second Meeting (1 to 1½ hours)

❏ 1. **Open in prayer**

❏ 2. **Sharing conversation**

❏ 3. **Review of initial meeting**

    ❏ Review of the 30-Day Diary

    ❏ Review of the revised budget (Monthly Income and Expense)

    ❏ Review of coaching particpant's spending decisions

    ❏ Reflect and adjust goals

    ❏ Review Debt Management Plan if Financial Hope was used

    ❏ Review homework assignment #1 and Quit Claim Deed

❏ 4. **Introduction of budgeting concepts**

    ❏ Envelope system

    ❏ Income Allocation Form

❏ 5. **Action Steps**

    ❏ Continue to adjust budget if needed

    ❏ Additional recommendations from coach

    ❏ Homework assignment #2

    ❏ Set date for next meeting

❏ 6. **Close in prayer**

MONTHLY INCOME AND EXPENSES

GROSS INCOME PER MONTH _____

    Salary _____

    Interest _____

    Dividends _____

    Other (_____) _____

    Other (_____) _____

LESS:

1. **Tithe** _____

2. **Tax** (Est. - Incl. Fed., State, FICA) _____

    NET SPENDABLE INCOME _____

3. **Housing** _____
    Mortgage (rent) _____
    Insurance _____
    Taxes _____
    Electricity _____
    Gas _____
    Water _____
    Sanitation _____
    Telephone _____
    Maintenance _____
    Other (_____) _____
    Other (_____) _____

4. **Food** _____

5. **Automobile(s)** _____
    Payments _____
    Gas and Oil _____
    Insurance _____
    License/Taxes _____
    Maint./Repair/Replace _____

6. **Insurance** _____
    Life _____
    Medical _____
    Other (_____) _____

7. **Debts** _____
    Credit Card _____
    Loans and Notes _____
    Other (_____) _____
    Other (_____) _____

8. **Enter./Recreation** _____
    Eating Out _____
    Baby Sitters _____
    Activities/Trips _____
    Vacation _____
    Other (_____) _____
    Other (_____) _____

9. **Clothing** _____

10. **Savings** _____

11. **Medical Expenses** _____
    Doctor _____
    Dentist _____
    Credit Card _____
    Other (_____) _____

12. **Miscellaneous** _____
    Toiletry, cosmetics _____
    Beauty, barber _____
    Laundry, cleaning _____
    Allowances, lunches _____
    Subscriptions _____
    Gifts (incl. Christmas) _____
    Cash _____
    Cable/Internet _____
    Other (_____) _____
    Other (_____) _____

13. **Investments** _____

14. **School/Child Care** _____
    Tuition _____
    Materials _____
    Transportation _____
    Day Care _____
    Other (_____) _____

TOTAL EXPENSES _____

INCOME VERSUS EXPENSES

    Net Spendable Income _____
    Less Expenses _____

15. **Unallocated Surplus Income**[1] _____

[1] This category is used when surplus income is received. This would be kept in the checking account to be used within a few weeks; otherwise, it should be transferred to an allocated category.

INDIVIDUAL ACCOUNT PAGE

_____ $_____ $_____
ACCOUNT CATEGORY   ALLOCATION   ALLOCATION

DATE	TRANSACTION	DEPOSIT	WITHDRAW	BALANCE

Crown Financial Ministries 2/03

INDIVIDUAL ACCOUNT PAGE

_____ $_____ $_____
ACCOUNT CATEGORY   ALLOCATION   ALLOCATION

DATE	TRANSACTION	DEPOSIT	WITHDRAW	BALANCE

Crown Financial Ministries 2/03

INCOME ALLOCATION

INCOME		INCOME SOURCE/PAY PERIOD			
BUDGET CATEGORY	**MONTHLY ALLOCATION**				
1. Tithe					
2. Tax					
3. Housing					
4. Food					
5. Auto					
6. Insurance					
7. Debts					
8. Entertainment/ Recreation					
9. Clothing					
10. Savings					
11. Medical/Dental					
12. Miscellaneous					
13. School/Child Care					
14. Investments					
15. Unallocated Surplus Income					

Crown Financial Ministries 2/03

ACTION STEPS

COACHING SESSION TWO

Becoming Debt Free

Key Scripture

"Just as the rich rule over the poor, so the borrower becomes the lender's servant" (Proverbs 22:7, TLB).

QUESTIONS TO ANSWER

1. **Read *Deuteronomy 15:4-6*; *Deuteronomy 28:1,2,12*; and *Deuteronomy 28:15,43-45*.** According to these passages how was debt viewed in the Old Testament?

What was the cause of someone getting in debt (becoming a borrower) or getting out of debt (becoming a lender)?

2. **Read *Romans 13:8*; *Proverbs 22:7*; and *1 Corinthians 7:23*.** Is debt encouraged in Scripture? Why?

   Romans 13:8—

   Proverbs 22:7—

How does this apply to you personally?

Do you have a plan to get out of debt? If you do, please describe it.

3. **Read *Psalm 37:21* and *Proverbs 3:27-28*.**
    What do these verses say about paying our debts?

    Psalm 37:21—

    Proverbs 3:27-28—

    How can you apply this to your life?

4. Scripture covers the topic of cosigning whenever it speaks of "surety" (being liable for another's debts) and "striking hands" (making pledges, whether by contract or handshake). Cosigning is pledging assets against the debt of another.)

    Read *Proverbs 22:26-27* and *Proverbs 17:18*.
    What does the Bible say about cosigning (striking hands, surety)?

    Proverbs 22:26-27—

    Proverbs 17:18—

    Then read *Proverbs 6:1-5*.
    If someone has cosigned, what should he or she attempt to do?

    How do these principles of cosigning apply to you?

We have so much personal debt in our nation that the average person has been described as someone driving on a bond-financed highway, in a bank-financed car, fueled by credit-card-financed gasoline, going to purchase furniture on an installment plan to put in a mortgaged home!

We are drowning in a sea of debt. In a recent year more than one million individuals filed bankruptcy in our country. And, more sobering, a Gallup Poll found that the majority of all those who had gone through a divorce indicated that financial tension at home was a major factor in the breakups.

Such financial tension was created largely by believing the "gospel" according to Madison Avenue: buy now and pay later with those easy monthly payments. We all know nothing about those monthly payments is easy. Advertisers fail to tell us the whole truth. They leave out one little word: debt.

The dictionary defines debt as: "Money or property which one person is obligated to pay to another."

WHAT IS DEBT?

The dictionary defines debt as: "Money or property which one person is obligated to pay to another." Debt includes money owed to credit card companies, bank loans, money borrowed from relatives, the home mortgage, and past due medical bills. Bills that come due, such as the monthly electrical bill, are not considered debt if they are paid on time.

WHAT DOES DEBT REALLY COST?

We need to understand the real cost of debt. Debt imposes both a fiscal and physical cost. For example, examine the true cost of credit card debt.

Assume you have $5,560 in credit card debt at an 18 percent interest rate and there are no tax consequences on the interest earned or spent. This would cost you $1,000 in interest annually. Study the chart on the next page.

Credit Card Debt of $5,560 at 18 Percent Interest				
Amount of interest you paid:				
Year 5	Year 10	Year 20	Year 30	Year 40
$5,000	$10,000	$20,000	$30,000	$40,000
What you would accumulate on $1,000 invested annually, earning 12 percent:				
Year 5	Year 10	Year 20	Year 30	Year 40
$6,353	$17,549	$72,052	$241,333	$767,091
How much the lender earns from your interest payment at 18 percent interest:				
Year 5	Year 10	Year 20	Year 30	Year 40
$7,154	$23,521	$146,628	$790,948	$4,163,213

You can see what lenders have known for a long time: the incredible impact of compounding interest working for them. Lenders will accumulate a total of $4,163,213 if you pay them $1,000 a year for 40 years, and they earn 18 percent on your payments! Is there any wonder that credit card companies are eager for you to become one of their borrowers?

Now compare the $40,000 you paid in interest over 40 years with the $767,091 you could have accumulated, earning 12 percent on $1,000 each year. The monthly income on $767,091 is $7,671 if it's earning 12 percent—without ever touching the principal.

Stop to consider this: Debt has a much higher cost than many realize. Next time you are tempted to purchase something with debt, ask yourself if the long-term benefits of staying out of debt outweigh the short-term benefits of the purchase.

THE PHYSICAL COST OF DEBT

Debt also extracts a physical toll. It often increases stress, which contributes to mental, physical, and emotional fatigue. It can stifle creativity and harm relationships. Many people raise their lifestyles through debt, only to discover that the burden of debt then controls their lifestyles. The car bumper sticker with, "I owe, I owe, it's off to work I go," is an unfortunate reality for too many people.

WHAT DOES SCRIPTURE SAY ABOUT DEBT?

The Bible does not say that it is sin to be in debt, but it does discourage indebtedness. Read the first portion of Romans 13:8 from several different Bible translations: *"Owe no man any thing"* (KJV). *"Let no debt remain outstanding"* (NIV). *"Pay all your debts"* (TLB). *"Owe nothing to anyone"* (NASB).

DEBT IS CONSIDERED SLAVERY

In Proverbs 22:7 we learn why our Lord discourages debt: *"Just as the rich rule the poor, so the borrower is servant to the lender"* (TLB). When we are in debt, we are in a position of servitude to the lender. The deeper we are in debt, the more like servants we become. We do not have the full freedom to decide where to spend our income. We legally have obligated ourselves to meet these debts.

DEBT MAY DENY GOD AN OPPORTUNITY

Ron Blue, an outstanding financial author, tells of a young man who wanted to go to seminary to become a missionary. The young man had no money and thought the only way he could afford to attend seminary was to secure a student loan. However, this would have encumbered him with $40,000 of debt by the time he graduated, which would have been impossible to pay back on a missionary's salary.

After a great deal of prayer, he decided to enroll without the help of a student loan and to trust the Lord to meet his needs. He graduated without borrowing anything and grew in his appreciation for how the sovereign, living God could creatively provide his needs. This was the most valuable lesson learned in seminary as he prepared for life on the mission field. Borrowing may deny God an opportunity to demonstrate His reality.

HOW TO GET OUT OF DEBT

There are six steps for getting out of debt. The steps are easy, but following them requires hard work. The goal is D-Day—Debtless Day—when you become absolutely free of debt.

1. Pray

In 2 Kings 4:1-7 a widow was threatened with losing her children to her creditor, and she appealed to Elisha for help. Elisha instructed the widow to borrow many empty jars from her neighbors. Then the Lord supernaturally multiplied her only possession—a small quantity of oil—and all the jars were filled. She sold the increased oil and paid her debts to free her children.

The same God who provided supernaturally for the widow is interested in your becoming free from debt. The first and most important step is to pray. Seek the Lord's help and guidance in your journey toward Debtless Day. Over a period of time, He can either act immedi-

"Just as the rich rule the poor, so the borrower is servant to the lender" (Proverbs 22:7, TLB).

ately, as in the case of the widow, or slowly. In either case, prayer is essential.

Your Money Map Coach will work with you to establish a budget. Listed below are the major steps to becoming debt free. Work with your coach as you determine a strategy and decide on financial goals. Your coach will be of immeasurable help to you as you learn to honor God with your finances. Forms are provided to assist you as you take each step.

2. Establish a budget

In our experience, few people in debt have been using a budget. They may have had one—neatly filed away in a drawer or loaded on their computer—but they have not been using it. A budget helps you plan ahead, evaluate your spending patterns, and control the biggest budget buster of them all: impulse spending. Crown has developed *Money Matters* software, which is an outstanding budgeting program for use on the computer.

3. List your assets—everything you own

Evaluate your assets to determine if there is anything you do not need that might be sold to help you to get out of debt more quickly. What about that set of golf clubs gathering dust in the garage? See if there is anything you can sell to enable you to get out of debt.

4. List your liabilities—everything you owe

Many people, particularly if they owe a lot of money, do not know exactly what they owe. It must be human nature: If I avoid unpleasant things, perhaps they will go away. However, you must list your debts to determine your current financial situation. You also need to list the interest rate your creditors are charging for each debt.

5. Establish a debt repayment for each creditor

If your unsecured debt is significant, you may benefit by visiting the Financial Hope Web site. See page 69 for an explanation. Otherwise, work with your coach to determine the following.

We suggest you decide which debts to pay off first, based on two factors.

- Pay off small debts first. You will be encouraged as they are eliminated, and this will free up cash to apply against other debts. After you pay off the first debt, apply its payment toward the next debt you want to retire. After the second debt is paid off, apply what you were paying on the first and second debts toward the next debt you want to eliminate, and so forth.

- Determine what rate of interest you are being charged on each debt, and try to pay off first the ones on which you paying the highest rate of interest.

6. Do not give up!

The last step is most difficult in getting out of debt. It is hard work getting out of debt, but the freedom of becoming debt free is worth the struggle.

AUTOMOBILE DEBT

Automobile debt is one of the leading causes of consumer indebtedness. Here's how to live free of car debt. First, decide in advance to keep your car for at least three years longer than your existing automobile debt. Second, pay off your automobile loan. Third, continue paying the monthly car payment, but pay it to yourself into a special savings account for your next car. Then, when you are ready to replace your car, the saved cash plus the trade-in should be sufficient to buy your car without credit. It may not be a new car, but you should be able to purchase a good, low-mileage, used car without any debt.

COSIGNING

Anytime you cosign, you become legally responsible for the debt of another. It is just as if you went to the bank, borrowed the money, and gave it to your friend or relative who is asking you to cosign.

A Federal Trade Commission study found that many of those who cosigned for bank loans ended up making the payments. Unfortunately, few cosigners plan for default.

Scripture speaks very clearly about cosigning. Proverbs 17:18 reads, *"It is poor judgment to countersign another's note, to become responsible for his debts"* (TLB). The words "poor judgment" are better translated "destitute of mind"!

A parent often cosigns for his or her child's first automobile. Consider modeling for your children the importance of not cosigning and using debt. Instead, train them to plan ahead and save for the cash purchase of their first cars.

Please use sound judgment and never cosign a note or become surety for any debt.

The freedom of becoming debt free is worth the struggle.

SESSION THREE OUTLINE

Third Meeting (1 to 1½ hours)

❏ 1. **Open in prayer**

❏ 2. **Review the revised budget** (Monthly Income and Expense)

❏ 3. **Review of coaching participant's spending decisions**

❏ 4. **Reflect on and adjust Goals**

❏ 5. **Review homework assignment #2**

❏ 6. **Review budgeting format chosen**

❏ 7. **Action Steps**
   - ❏ Continue to refine budget
   - ❏ Additional recommendations from coach
   - ❏ Homework assignment #3
   - ❏ Set date for next meeting

❏ 8. **Close in prayer**

MONTHLY INCOME AND EXPENSES

GROSS INCOME PER MONTH _____
- Salary _____
- Interest _____
- Dividends _____
- Other (_____) _____
- Other (_____) _____

LESS:

1. **Tithe** _____

2. **Tax** (Est. - Incl. Fed., State, FICA) _____

   NET SPENDABLE INCOME _____

3. **Housing** _____
   - Mortgage (rent) _____
   - Insurance _____
   - Taxes _____
   - Electricity _____
   - Gas _____
   - Water _____
   - Sanitation _____
   - Telephone _____
   - Maintenance _____
   - Other (_____) _____
   - Other (_____) _____

4. **Food** _____

5. **Automobile(s)** _____
   - Payments _____
   - Gas and Oil _____
   - Insurance _____
   - License/Taxes _____
   - Maint./Repair/Replace _____

6. **Insurance** _____
   - Life _____
   - Medical _____
   - Other (_____) _____

7. **Debts** _____
   - Credit Card _____
   - Loans and Notes _____
   - Other (_____) _____
   - Other (_____) _____

8. **Enter./Recreation** _____
   - Eating Out _____
   - Baby Sitters _____
   - Activities/Trips _____
   - Vacation _____
   - Other (_____) _____
   - Other (_____) _____

9. **Clothing** _____

10. **Savings** _____

11. **Medical Expenses** _____
    - Doctor _____
    - Dentist _____
    - Credit Card _____
    - Other (_____) _____

12. **Miscellaneous** _____
    - Toiletry, cosmetics _____
    - Beauty, barber _____
    - Laundry, cleaning _____
    - Allowances, lunches _____
    - Subscriptions _____
    - Gifts (incl. Christmas) _____
    - Cash _____
    - Cable/Internet _____
    - Other (_____) _____
    - Other (_____) _____

13. **Investments** _____

14. **School/Child Care** _____
    - Tuition _____
    - Materials _____
    - Transportation _____
    - Day Care _____
    - Other (_____) _____

TOTAL EXPENSES _____

INCOME VERSUS EXPENSES

Net Spendable Income _____
Less Expenses _____

_____

15. **Unallocated Surplus Income**[1] _____

[1] This category is used when surplus income is received. This would be kept in the checking account to be used within a few weeks; otherwise, it should be transferred to an allocated category.

COACHING SESSION THREE

Contentment and Peace

QUESTIONS TO ANSWER

1. **Read *Joshua 1:8* and *Hebrews 11:36-40*.**
   What do each of these passages communicate to you about financial prosperity for the believer?

   Joshua 1:8—

   Hebrews 11:36-40—

   Consider the lives of Job, Joseph, and Paul. Did these men ever experience periods of financial abundance as well as times of financial hardship?

   Was their lack of financial prosperity a result of sin and lack of faith?

   Should all Christians always prosper financially? Why?

   Read *Psalm 73:1-20*.
   What does this passage tell you about the prosperity of the wicked?

How does this impact your thinking?

2. **Read *Luke 12:15*; *Ephesians 5:3,5*; and *Colossians 3:5*.**
   What do each of these passages say about coveting and greed?

   Luke 12:15—

   Ephesians 5:3,5—

   Colossians 3:5—

   Do you personally struggle with coveting or greed? How do you propose to conquer these sins?

3. **Read *Philippians 4:11-14* and *1 Timothy 6:6-8*.**
   What do each of these passages communicate to you about contentment?

   Philippians 4:11-14—

   1 Timothy 6:6-8—

   How does our way of life discourage contentment?

   What changes do you need to make in your personal life so that you can live a contented life? How do you plan to accomplish these changes?

4. **Read *Mark 8:36-38; Acts 4:32-37;* and *1 Thessalonians 4:11-12*.**

What do these passages communicate to you about our priorities and the way we live?

Mark 8:36-38—

Acts 4:32-37—

1 Thessalonians 4:11-12—

Do the following factors influence what you buy and how you live? Describe the impact of each factor in your personal life.

- Comparing your lifestyle with that of friends and other people—

- Television, magazines, catalogs, and other advertisements—

- Your study of the Bible—

- Your commitment to Christ and to things that are important to Him—

Do you sense that the Lord wants you to alter any part of your standard of living? If so, what?

NOTES TO READ

Many people experiencing financial challenges find it difficult to experience God's peace and contentment. However, the Lord wants us to enjoy the true contentment and peace that only He can give us.

CONTENTMENT

First Timothy 6:8 issues this challenging statement: *"If we have food and covering, with these we shall be content."* Study this passage carefully. It declares that if you have food and covering (clothes and shelter) you should be content. Our culture has restated this verse to read something like, "If you can afford the finest food, wear the latest fashions, drive the newest luxury automobile, live in a beautiful home, then you can be happy." Our culture is a materialistic, consumption-oriented society that operates on the assumptions that more is always better and happiness is based on acquiring possessions.

The word "contentment" is mentioned seven times in Scripture, and six times it has to do with money. The apostle Paul wrote, *"I have learned to be content in whatever circumstances I am. I know how to get along with humble means, and I also know how to live in prosperity; in any and every circumstance I have learned the secret of being filled and going hungry, both of having abundance and suffering need. I can do all things through Him who strengthens me"* (Philippians 4:11-13). Review this passage. Paul "learned" to be content. We are not born content; rather, we learn contentment.

There are three elements to the secret of contentment.

1. Know what God requires of a steward—how to manage the possessions entrusted to you.

2. Fulfill those requirements.

3. Trust God to faithfully do His part.

Note carefully that it is not just knowing these things that brings contentment; it is doing them. Once we have been faithful in the doing, we can be content in knowing that our loving heavenly Father will entrust the precise quantity of possessions He knows will be best for us at any particular time—whether much or little.

Biblical contentment is an inner peace that accepts what God has chosen for our present vocation, station in life, and financial state. Scripture emphasizes this: *"Let your way of life be free from the love of money, being content with what you have; for He Himself has said, 'I will never desert you, nor will I ever forsake you' "* (Hebrews 13:5).

In the area of finances, contentment does not mean complacency. Complacency means that I have a problem and I suffer through it with a good attitude, but contentment means that I know I'm in the center of God's will. I change the things I can; the things I can't change I am willing to accept and be content with, because I know the One who is in control. The secret of a happy life is learning how to deal with both the good times and the bad and, like the apostle Paul, knowing how to be content with either.

DISCONTENTMENT

It's helpful to recognize that there are a number of factors that contribute to a sense of discontentment.

1. Compare your lifestyle to others

Some use comparison to justify spending more than they should. Many have suffered financially because they tried but could not afford to "keep up with the Joneses." Someone once said, "You can never keep up with the Joneses. Just about the time you've caught them, they go deeper in debt to buy more things!"

2. Avoid coveting

Coveting means to desire another person's property. Coveting is expressly prohibited throughout Scripture. The last of the Ten Commandments reads, *"You shall not covet your neighbor's house; you shall not covet your neighbor's wife or his male servant or his female servant or his ox or his donkey or anything that belongs to your neighbor"* (Exodus 20:17). The Lord prohibited coveting with an infinitely broad application ("or anything that belongs to your neighbor"). In other words, we are commanded not to covet anything that belongs to anyone!

A greedy or covetous person is an idolater. *"Immorality or any impurity or greed must not even be named among you . . . For this you know with certainty, that no immoral or impure person or covetous man, who is an idolater, has an inheritance in the kingdom of Christ and God"* (Ephesians 5:3,5). Ask the Lord to show you if you are guilty of coveting what is another's. If so, ask the Lord to change your heart.

> *Contentment means that I know I'm in the center of God's will.*

3. Don't be conformed to this world

Romans 12:2 begins with this command, *"Do not be conformed to this world."* The Amplified version reads this way: *"Do not be conformed to this world—this age, fashioned after and adapted to its external, superficial customs"* (Romans 12:2). We live in what probably is the most affluent culture in the history of the world. We are constantly bombarded with costly, manipulative advertising. The purpose of advertising is to prompt us to spend money. Advertisers usually stress the importance of image rather than function. For example, automobile ads rarely focus on a car as reliable transportation that is economical to operate. Instead, an image of status or sex appeal is projected.

Reflect on the claims of most commercials. No matter what the product–clothing, deodorants, credit cards, you name it—the message is communicated that the "beautiful, wrinkle-free life" can be ours if we are willing to buy it. Unfortunately, to some extent this has influenced all of us. Author George Fooshee so aptly states, "People buy things they do not need with money they do not have to impress people they do not even like."

4. Have an eternal perspective

Recognize and nurture an eternal perspective. Almost everything in our culture and in the media implores us to focus on the immediate. Advertisers persuade purchasers to gratify themselves today with no thought of tomorrow. To understand how brief life is on earth, picture life as follows.

Our momentary time on earth is but a dot on the timeline of eternity. Yet we have the opportunity to affect eternity by how we handle money. We not only have the privilege to lay up treasures for ourselves in heaven but we are able to spend money to influence people for Jesus Christ. Gaining an eternal perspective and eternal values will have a profound effect on your decision making.

As an adult, have you ever returned to a place you knew as a child? If so, you've probably been shocked to discover how small it really was!

"And be not conformed to this world, but be ye transformed by the renewing of your mind, that ye may prove what is that good, and acceptable, and perfect, will of God" (Romans 12:2, KJV).

Do you remember wanting to get something so much that it consumed all your thoughts? Yet now it means almost nothing to you? We think we will experience something similar when we arrive in heaven. Many things that loom so large and important to us now will fade into insignificance in the light of eternity. We can either live with a view toward eternity or live with our focus on this present world.

GOD'S PEACE

The basis for experiencing God's peace is knowing the Lord and understanding how much He loves and cares for you. Read these verses slowly and allow the Lord to express His care for you.

"The steadfast of mind You will keep in perfect peace, because he trusts in You" (Isaiah 26:3).

"What then shall we say to these things? If God is for us, who is against us?" (Romans 8:31).

"Be anxious for nothing, but in everything by prayer and supplication with thanksgiving let your requests be made known to God. And the peace of God, which surpasses all comprehension, will guard your hearts and your minds in Christ Jesus" (Philippians 4:6-7).

"Peace I leave with you; My peace I give to you; not as the world gives do I give to you. Do not let your heart be troubled, nor let it be fearful" (John 14:27).

"These things have I [Jesus] spoken to you, so that in Me you may have peace. In the world you have tribulation, but take courage; I have overcome the world" (John 16:33).

POVERTY, PROSPERITY, OR STEWARDSHIP?

Some Christians embrace one of two extremes. On one end of the spectrum are those who believe that godliness can occur only in poverty. However, the Bible does not say that a godly person must live in poverty. A number of godly people in Scripture were among the wealthiest people of their day. In the Old Testament the Lord extended the reward of abundance to the children of Israel when they were obedient, but the threat of poverty was one of the consequences of disobedience. God's Word says, *"I have set before you today life and prosperity, and death and adversity; in that I command you today to love the Lord your God, to walk in*

"The steadfast of mind You will keep in perfect peace because he trusts in You" (Isaiah 26:3).

His ways and to keep His commandments . . . that the Lord your God may bless you" (Deuteronomy 30:15-16).

At the other end of spectrum lies the belief that all Christians who have faith will always prosper. This extreme is also in error. Study the life of Joseph. He was born into a prosperous family, thrown into a pit, and finally sold into slavery by his jealous brothers. While Joseph was a slave, his master promoted him to be head of his household. Later he made the righteous decision not to commit adultery with his master's wife, yet he was thrown in jail for years because of that decision. In God's timing, he ultimately was elevated to prime minister of Egypt.

The guideline for prosperity is found in Scripture: *"This book of the law shall not depart from your mouth, but you shall meditate on it day and night, so that you may be careful to do according to all that is written in it; for then you will make your way prosperous, and then you will have success"* (Joshua 1:8).

Two requirements for prosperity become apparent from studying this passage. You must meditate on the Scriptures, and you are required to do all that is written in them. Once you have fulfilled these obligations, you place yourself in the position to be blessed financially, but there is no guarantee that the godly will always experience financial prosperity. There are three reasons the godly may not prosper.

1. Violating scriptural principles

Look again at Joshua 1:8. There is the requirement to do according to *all* that is written in the Bible. You may be giving generously but acting dishonestly. You may be honest but not fulfilling your work responsibilities. You may be a faithful employee but head-over-heels in debt. Those who do not understand all the requirements often neglect critical areas of responsibility unknowingly and suffer financially.

2. Building godly character

Romans 5:3-4 reads, *"Tribulation brings about perseverance; and perseverance, proven character."* Many godly people in the Bible went through periods when they were living righteously, yet lost their possessions. David became a national hero after slaying Goliath. David served blamelessly, only to be forced to flee for his life from a tormented King Saul. Paul learned the secret of contentment while being held captive in chains and suffering want, even though he was righteous.

God sometimes molds our character by allowing us to experience difficult circumstances. In His infinite wisdom He knows exactly how much He can entrust to us at any time without it harming our relationship with Him.

3. Our dependence

A father was carrying his two-year-old child as he waded in a lake. When they were close to shore, the child was unconcerned because of the apparent safety of the beach, even though the water was deep enough to drown him. He didn't understand his dependence on his father. However, the farther they moved away from shore, the tighter the child held to his father. Like the child, we are always completely dependent on the Lord to provide for us. However, often we don't recognize our dependence when we are "close to shore," experiencing the apparent security of financial prosperity. But when our possessions are few, it is easier to recognize our need and to cling to our heavenly Father.

Let's summarize: The Scriptures teach neither the necessity of poverty nor uninterrupted prosperity. What the Bible teaches is the responsibility of being a faithful steward.

YOU CAN KNOW THE LORD

If you successfully apply all the financial principles of Scripture, you will not experience true peace and contentment unless you know Jesus Christ as your personal Savior and Lord. The following five steps describe how you can enter into this relationship with the Lord.

1. God loves you and wants you to experience a meaningful life.

God created people in His own image, and He desires an intimate relationship with each of us. *"For God so loved the world, that He gave His only begotten Son, that whoever believes in Him shall not perish, but have eternal life"* (John 3:16). *"I [Jesus] came that they might have life, and might have it abundantly"* (John 10:10). God the Father loved you so much that He gave His only Son, Jesus Christ, to die for you.

2. Unfortunately, we are separated from God.

God is holy, which means God is perfect, and He cannot have a relationship with anyone who is not perfect. Every person has sinned, and the consequence of sin is separation from God. *"For all have sinned and*

God sometimes molds our character by allowing us to experience difficult circumstances.

fall short of the glory of God" (Romans 3:23). *"Your sins have cut you off from God"* (Isaiah 59:2, TLB).

The diagram below illustrates an enormous gap that separates people from God. Individuals try without success to bridge this gap through their own efforts, such as philosophy, religion, material goods, charitable activity, or living a good moral life.

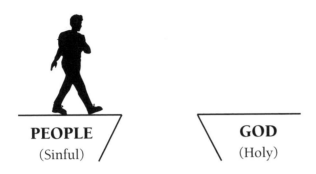

PEOPLE
(Sinful)

GOD
(Holy)

3.   God's only provision to bridge this gap is Jesus Christ.

Jesus Christ died on the cross to pay the penalty for our sin. He bridged the gap between us and God. *"Jesus said to him, 'I am the way, and the truth, and the life; no one comes to the Father but through Me' "* (John 14:6). *"But God demonstrates His own love toward us, in that while we were yet sinners, Christ died for us"* (Romans 5:8). *"That if you confess with your mouth Jesus as Lord, and believe in your heart that God raised Him from the dead, you will be saved"* (Romans 10:9).

This diagram illustrates our union with God through Jesus Christ.

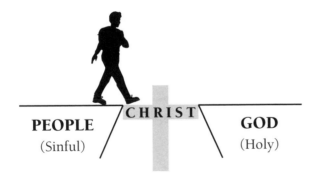

PEOPLE
(Sinful)

CHRIST

GOD
(Holy)

4. This relationship is a gift from God.

By an act of faith we can receive the free gift of a relationship with God. *"By grace you have been saved through faith; and that not of yourselves, it is the gift of God; not as a result of works, so that no one may boast"* (Ephesians 2:8-9).

5. We must each receive Jesus Christ individually.

We need to ask Jesus Christ to come into our lives, forgive us of our sins, and to be our Savior and Lord.

If you want to know the Lord or are uncertain whether you have this relationship, you may receive Christ by praying a prayer similar to this one: *"Father God, I need You. I invite Jesus to come into my life as my Savior and Lord and make me the person You want me to be. Thank You for forgiving my sins and giving me the gift of eternal life."*

Nothing in life compares to knowing Christ. If you asked Christ into your life, please tell your coach, who will be able to guide you to those who will assist you in your spiritual growth.

JOURNEY TO
FINANCIAL FREEDOM

SESSION FOUR OUTLINE

Fourth Meeting (1 to 1½ hours)

❏ 1. **Open in prayer and general conversation**

❏ 2. **Review the revised budget** (Monthly Income and Expense)

❏ 3. **Review of coaching participant's spending decisions**

❏ 4. **Reflect on and adjust Goals** (change if necessary)

❏ 5. **Review homework assignment #3**

❏ 6. **Action Steps**
  ❏ Continue to refine budget
  ❏ Additional recommendations from coach
  ❏ Homework assignments #4 and #5
  ❏ Encourage involvement in additional study (small group, seminar)
  ❏ Set date for next meeting

❏ 7. **Close in prayer**

MONTHLY INCOME AND EXPENSES

GROSS INCOME PER MONTH _____

   Salary _____

   Interest _____

   Dividends _____

   Other (_____) _____

   Other (_____) _____

LESS:

  1. Tithe _____

  2. Tax (Est. - Incl. Fed., State, FICA) _____

  NET SPENDABLE INCOME _____

  3. Housing _____

    Mortgage (rent) _____

    Insurance _____

    Taxes _____

    Electricity _____

    Gas _____

    Water _____

    Sanitation _____

    Telephone _____

    Maintenance _____

    Other (_____) _____

    Other (_____) _____

  4. Food _____

  5. Automobile(s) _____

    Payments _____

    Gas and Oil _____

    Insurance _____

    License/Taxes _____

    Maint./Repair/Replace _____

  6. Insurance _____

    Life _____

    Medical _____

    Other (_____) _____

  7. Debts _____

    Credit Card _____

    Loans and Notes _____

    Other (_____) _____

    Other (_____) _____

  8. Enter./Recreation _____

    Eating Out _____

    Baby Sitters _____

    Activities/Trips _____

    Vacation _____

    Other (_____) _____

    Other (_____) _____

  9. Clothing _____

 10. Savings _____

 11. Medical Expenses _____

    Doctor _____

    Dentist _____

    Credit Card _____

    Other (_____) _____

 12. Miscellaneous _____

    Toiletry, cosmetics _____

    Beauty, barber _____

    Laundry, cleaning _____

    Allowances, lunches _____

    Subscriptions _____

    Gifts (incl. Christmas) _____

    Cash _____

    Cable/Internet _____

    Other (_____) _____

    Other (_____) _____

 13. Investments _____

 14. School/Child Care _____

    Tuition _____

    Materials _____

    Transportation _____

    Day Care _____

    Other (_____) _____

TOTAL EXPENSES _____

INCOME VERSUS EXPENSES

  Net Spendable Income _____

  Less Expenses _____

 15. Unallocated Surplus Income[1] _____

[1] This category is used when surplus income is received. This would be kept in the checking account to be used within a few weeks; otherwise, it should be transferred to an allocated category.

Crown Financial Ministries 2/03

COACHING SESSION FOUR

Giving and Saving

KEY SCRIPTURE

"Remember the words of the Lord Jesus, that He Himself said, 'It is more blessed to give than to receive'" (Acts 20:35).

QUESTIONS TO ANSWER

Answer these questions before reading the Notes on pages 54-60.

1. **Read *1 Corinthians 13:3* and *2 Corinthians 9:7-8*.**
   What do these passages communicate about the importance of the proper attitude in giving?

   1 Corinthians 13:3—

   2 Corinthians 9:7-8—

   After prayerfully evaluating your attitude in giving, how would you describe it?

2. **Read *Acts 20:35*.**
   How does this principle from God's economy differ from the way most people view giving?

List the benefits for the giver that are found in each of the following passages.

Proverbs 11:24-25—

Matthew 6:20—

Luke 12:34—

3. **Read 2 Corinthians 8:1-5.**
   Identify three principles from this passage that should influence how much you give.

   ■

   ■

   ■

   Prayerfully (with your spouse if you are married) seek the Lord's guidance to determine how much you should give.

4. **Read Genesis 41:34-36; Proverbs 21:20; and Proverbs 30:24-25.**
   What do these passages communicate to you about savings?

   Genesis 41:34-36—

   Proverbs 21:20—

   Proverbs 30:24-25—

How do you propose to begin saving if you are not yet saving?

5. Gambling is defined as playing games of chance for money, betting, taking great risks, and speculating. Some of today's most common forms of gambling are casino wagering; betting on sporting events, horse races, dog races; and state lotteries. What are some of the motivations that cause people to gamble?

Do these motives please the Lord? Why?

Read *Proverbs 28:20* **and** *Proverbs 28:22.*
According to these passages, why do you think a godly person should not gamble?

In this lesson we will explore God's perspective of giving and saving.

GIVING

Few areas of the Christian life can be more frustrating or rewarding than that of giving. If you understand God's perspective of giving and do it, giving becomes a blessing.

ATTITUDES IN GIVING

God evaluates our giving on the basis of our attitude. God's attitude in giving is best summed up in John 3:16: *"For God so loved the world, that He gave His only begotten Son."* Because God loved, He gave. He set the example of giving motivated by love.

An attitude of love in giving is crucial: *"If I give all my possessions to feed the poor . . . but do not have love, it profits me nothing"* (1 Corinthians 13:3). It is hard to imagine anything more commendable than giving everything to the poor; but, if it is done with the wrong attitude—without love—it is no benefit whatsoever to the giver.

> *"For God so loved the world, that He gave His only begotten Son"* (John 3:16).

The only way you can give out of a heart filled with love is to recognize that your gifts are actually given to the Lord Himself. An example of this perspective is found in Numbers 18:24: *"For the tithe of the sons of Israel, which they offer as an offering to the Lord, I have given to the Levites for an inheritance."* If giving is merely to a church, a ministry, or a needy person, it is only charity; but, if it is to the Lord, it becomes an act of worship. Because God is our Creator, our Savior, and our Faithful Provider, we can express our gratefulness and love by giving our gifts to Him.

For example, when the offering plate is being passed at church, we should consciously remind ourselves that we are giving our gift to the Lord Himself.

In addition to giving out of a heart filled with love, we are to give cheerfully. *"Each one must do just as he has purposed in his heart, not grudgingly or under compulsion, for God loves a cheerful giver"* (2 Corinthians 9:7).

Stop and examine yourself. What is your attitude toward giving?

ADVANTAGES OF GIVING

According to God's economy, if a gift is given with the proper attitude, the giver benefits more than the receiver. *"Remember the words of the Lord Jesus, that He Himself said, 'It is more blessed to give than to receive' "* (Acts 20:35). As we examine Scripture, we find that the giver benefits in three areas.

1. Increase in intimacy

Above all else, giving directs our attention and hearts to Christ. *"For where your treasure is, there your heart will be also"* (Matthew 6:21). This is why it is so necessary to go through the process of consciously giving each gift to the person of Jesus Christ. When you give your gift to Him, your heart will automatically be drawn to the Lord. And nothing in life can compare to entering into His joy and knowing Christ more intimately.

2. Increase in Heaven

God's Word says, *"But store up for yourselves treasures in heaven, where neither moth nor rust destroys, and where thieves do not break in or steal"* (Matthew 6:20). The Lord tells us that there really is something akin to the "First National Bank of Heaven," and He wants us to know that we can invest for eternity.

The apostle Paul wrote, *"Not that I seek the gift itself, but I seek for the profit which increases to your account"* (Philippians 4:17). There is an account for each of us in heaven, which we will be privileged to enjoy for eternity. Even though it is true that we "can't take it with us," Scripture teaches that we can make deposits to our heavenly account before we die.

3. Increase on Earth

Many people do not believe that giving results in material blessings flowing to the giver—only spiritual blessings. However, Scripture says, *"There is one who scatters, yet increases all the more, and there is one who withholds what is justly due, and yet it results only in want. The generous man will be prosperous, and he who waters will himself be watered"* (Proverbs 11:24-25).

Examine this Scripture passage. *"He who sows sparingly shall also reap sparingly, and he who sows bountifully shall also reap bountifully . . . God is*

> *"The generous man will be prosperous, and he who waters will himself be watered"* (Proverbs 11:25).

"Honor the Lord from your wealth, and from the first of all your produce" (Proverbs 3:9).

able to make all grace abound to you, so that always having all sufficiency in everything, you may have an abundance for every good deed; as it is written, 'He scattered abroad, he gave to the poor, His righteousness endures forever.' Now He who supplies seed to the sower and bread for food, will supply and multiply your seed for sowing and increase the harvest of your righteousness; you will be enriched in everything for all liberality" (2 Corinthians 9:6,8-11).

Note carefully in that verse *why* the Lord is returning an increase materially: *"Always having all sufficiency in everything, you may have an abundance for every good deed . . . [He] will supply and multiply your seed for sowing . . . you will be enriched in everything for all liberality."* The Lord produces a material increase so that we may give more and have our needs met at the same time.

When we give, we should do so with a sense of expectancy—anticipating the Lord to provide a material increase but not knowing when or how the Lord may choose to provide this increase.

PRIORITY OF GIVING

"Honor the Lord from your wealth and from the first of all your produce" (Proverbs 3:9). As soon as we receive any income we should set aside the amount we are going to give. This habit helps us to remember to put Christ first in all we do and defeats the temptation to spend on ourselves the portion we have decided to give.

AMOUNT TO GIVE

In the Old Testament the tithe (10 percent) was the standard. *"Will a man rob God? Yet you are robbing Me! But you say, 'How have we robbed You?' In tithes and offerings. You are cursed with a curse, for you are robbing Me, the whole nation of you!"* (Malachi 3:8-9).

In the New Testament the tithe is neither specifically rejected nor specifically recommended. What is taught is giving in proportion to the material blessing one has received, with special commendation for sacrificial giving. We are convinced that we should tithe as a minimum and then give over and above the tithe as the Lord prospers or directs us.

PLACES FOR GIVING

The local church and ministries

Throughout its pages the Bible encourages us to give to fund the work and workers of God. *"Pastors who do their work well should be paid well and should be highly appreciated, especially those who work hard at both preaching and teaching"* (1 Timothy 5:17, TLB). *"The one who is taught the word is to share all good things with the one who teaches"* (Galatians 6:6).

The poor

Read carefully one of the most exciting and yet sobering truths in Scripture: *"The King will say . . . 'For I was hungry, and you gave Me something to eat; I was thirsty, and you gave Me something to drink . . .' Then the righteous will answer Him, 'Lord, when did we see You hungry, and feed You, or thirsty, and give You something to drink? . . .' The King will answer and say to them, 'Truly I say to you, to the extent that you did it to one of these brothers of Mine, even the least of them, you did it to Me.' Then He will say to those on His left, 'Depart from Me, accursed ones, into the eternal fire . . . for I was hungry, and you gave Me nothing to eat; I was thirsty, and you gave Me nothing to drink . . . To the extent that you did not do it to one of the least of these, you did not do it to Me'"* (Matthew 25:34-45).

In some mysterious way, Jesus, the Creator of all things, personally identifies Himself with the poor. When we share with the poor we are actually sharing with Jesus Himself. And if that truth is staggering, then the reciprocal is terrifying: When we do not give to the poor, we leave Christ hungry and thirsty.

Although the area of giving can be challenging, if done with the proper attitude, it can be one of the most exciting and vibrant parts of your Christian experience.

SAVING

Scripture encourages us to save. *"The wise man saves for the future, but the foolish man spends whatever he gets"* (Proverbs 21:20, TLB). The ant is commended for saving for a future need. *"Four things on earth are small, yet they are extremely wise; ants are creatures of little strength, yet they store up their food in the summer"* (Proverbs 30:24-25, NIV).

Saving requires self-denial. Joseph saved during seven years of plenty in order to survive during seven years of famine. That is what saving is: denying an expenditure today so you will have something to spend in the future. One of the major reasons most people are poor savers is that our culture does not practice self-denial. When we want something, we want it now!

When we share with the poor we are actually sharing with Jesus Himself.

> *"Steady plodding brings prosperity; hasty speculation brings poverty"* (Proverbs 21:5, TLB).

HOW TO SAVE AND HOW MUCH TO SAVE

The most effective way to save is to save regularly. When you receive income, the first check you write should be for the Lord and the second check for your savings. An automatic payroll deduction can ensure that a portion of your income is saved regularly. Some commit to savings income from tax refunds or bonuses. If you immediately save a portion of your income each time you are paid, you will save more.

The Bible does not teach an amount or percentage to be saved. We recommend saving 10 percent of your income. This may not be possible initially, but begin the habit of saving—even if only a dollar a month. Many financial experts recommend you save the equivalent of three to six months of income for emergencies.

INVESTING

People place some of their savings in investments with the expectation of receiving an income and/or growth in value. The purpose and intention of Crown Financial Ministries is not to recommend any specific investments. No one is authorized to use affiliation with Crown Financial Ministries to promote the sale of any investments or financial services. Our objective is to draw attention to the scriptural framework for savings and investing. Visit Crown's Web site at www.crown.org for more detailed information on investing. The following biblical principles apply to investing.

STEADY PLODDING

"Steady plodding brings prosperity; hasty speculation brings poverty" (Proverbs 21:5, TLB). The original Hebrew words for "steady plodding" picture a person filling a large barrel one handful at a time. Little by little the barrel is filled to overflowing. The fundamental principle you need to practice to become a successful investor is to spend less than you earn. Then save and invest the difference over a long period of time.

Examine various investments. Almost all of them are well suited for "steady plodding." Your home mortgage is paid off after years of steady payments. Savings grow because of compounding interest, and your business can increase steadily in value through the years.

AVOID RISKY INVESTMENTS

"There is another serious problem I have seen everywhere—savings are put

into risky investments that turn sour, and soon there is nothing left to pass on to one's son. The man who speculates is soon back to where he began—with nothing" (Ecclesiastes 5:13-15, TLB). Scripture clearly warns of avoiding risky investments, yet each year thousands of people lose money in highly speculative and sometimes fraudulent investments.

UNDERSTANDING COMPOUND INTEREST

Understanding compounding is crucial. There are three variables in compounding: the amount, the percentage rate you earn, and the length of time you save.

1. The amount

The amount you save will be dictated by your level of income, the cost of your standard of living, how much debt you have, and how faithfully you budget. It is our hope that you will increase the amount available for saving as you implement these biblical principles.

2. Rate of return

The second variable is the rate of interest you earn on an investment. The following table demonstrates how an investment of $1,000 a year grows at various interest rates.

Interest	Year 5	Year 10	Year 20	Year 30	Year 40
6%	5,975	13,972	38,993	83,802	164,048
8%	6,336	15,645	49,423	122,346	279,781
10%	6,716	17,531	63,003	180,943	486,851
12%	7,115	19,655	80,699	270,293	859,142

As you can see, the increase in the rate of return has a remarkable effect on the amount accumulated. A 2 percent increase almost doubles the amount over 40 years. However, be careful not to invest in too risky an investment in order to achieve a high return. Usually the higher the rate, the higher the risk.

3. Time

Time is an element we cannot control. However, we can start saving now. Answer this question: Who do you think would accumulate more by age 65: a person who started to save $1,000 a year at age 21, saved for eight years, and then completely stopped, or a person who saved $1,000 a year for 37 years who started at age 29—both earning 10 per-

"Render to Caesar the things that are Caesar's" (Luke 20:22-25).

cent on their savings? Is it the person who saved a total of $8,000 or the one who saved $37,000? Incredibly, the person who saved only $8,000 accumulated more because that person started saving earlier. The moral of this illustration: Start saving now.

GAMBLING AND LOTTERIES

Government-sanctioned lotteries and gambling of all types are sweeping our country. The Bible does not specifically prohibit gambling. However, many gamble in an attempt to *get rich quick*, which is a violation of Scripture.

Sadly, hundreds of thousands of compulsive gamblers regularly deplete their family incomes. Their stories are heartbreaking. We believe a godly person should never participate in gambling or lotteries–even for entertainment. We should not expose ourselves to the risk of becoming compulsive gamblers; nor should we support an industry that enslaves so many.

TAXES

What is the biblical perspective on paying taxes? That is the same question that was asked of Jesus. *"Is it lawful for us to pay taxes to Caesar or not? . . . [Jesus] said to them, 'Show Me a denarius [Roman coin]. Whose likeness and inscription does it have?' They said, 'Caesar's.' And He said to them, 'Then render to Caesar the things that are Caesar's' "* (Luke 20:22-25). This is an example of the contrast between the practices of our society and the teaching of Scripture.

The Bible tells us we should pay taxes. *"Every person is to be in subjection to the governing authorities. For there is no authority except from God, and those which exist are established by God . . . Because of this you also pay taxes, for rulers are servants of God, devoting themselves to this very thing. Render to all what is due them: tax to whom tax is due"* (Romans 13:1,6-7).

JOURNEY TO FINANCIAL FREEDOM

SESSION FIVE OUTLINE

Fifth Meeting (1 to 1½ hours)

❏ 1. **Open in prayer and general conversation**

❏ 2. **Review of coaching participant's spending decisions**

❏ 3. **Reflect on and adjust Goals** (change if necessary)

❏ 4. **Review homework assignments #4 and #5**

❏ 5. **Action Steps**
   - ❏ Continue to refine budget
   - ❏ Additional recommendations from coach
   - ❏ Encourage involvement in additional study (small group, seminar, or to become a Money Map Coach)
   - ❏ Set date for next meeting, if necessary

❏ 6. **Close in prayer**

Coaching Session Five

Family

> ## Key Scripture
> *"Train up a child in the way he should go, even when he is old he will not depart from it"* (Proverbs 22:6).

QUESTIONS TO ANSWER

Answer these questions before reading the Notes on pages 69-73.

1. **Read *Matthew 15:4-6* and *1 Timothy 5:8*.**

   Does the Bible require us to take care of our family members?

   How does this apply in your situation?

2. **Read *Proverbs 1:8-9*.**

   Who should be among your counselors?

   In your opinion, who should be the husband's number one human counselor? The wife's? Why?

3. **Read *Deuteronomy 6:6-7; Deuteronomy 11:18-19; Proverbs 22:6;* and *Ephesians 6:4*.**

   According to these passages, who is responsible for teaching children how to handle money from a biblical perspective?

   Stop and reflect for a few minutes: Describe how well were you prepared to manage money when you first left home as a young person?

4. **Describe how you are going to teach your children to:**

Give generously—

Spend wisely—

Keep out of debt—

Save—

Invest—

5. **Read *Genesis 24:35-36; Proverbs 13:22;* and *2 Corinthians 12:14.***
Should parents attempt to leave a material inheritance to their children?

How are you going to implement this principle?

Then read *Proverbs 20:21* and *Galatians 4:1-2.*
What caution should a parent exercise?

Proverbs 20:21—

Galatians 4:1-2—

Women tend to be gifted with a wonderfully sensitive and intuitive nature that is usually very accurate.

TAKE CARE OF FAMILY MEMBERS

In our culture we are experiencing a tragic breakdown in the area of taking care of our family. Husbands have failed to provide for their wives, parents have neglected their children, and grown sons and daughters have forsaken their elderly parents. Such neglect is solemnly condemned. *"If anyone does not provide for his own, and especially for those of his household, he has denied the faith, and is worse than an unbeliever"* (1 Timothy 5:8). Meeting the needs of your family and relatives is a priority—one in which there should be no compromise.

HUSBAND AND WIFE COMMUNICATION

If you are married, the first person you need to consult is your spouse. Permit us to be blunt. Regardless of your spouse's business background or financial aptitude, you must cultivate and seek your spouse's counsel. Women tend to be gifted with a wonderfully sensitive and intuitive nature that is usually very accurate. Men tend to focus objectively on the facts. The husband and wife need each other to achieve the proper balance for a correct decision. We also believe that the Lord honors the wife's "office" or "position" as helpmate to her husband. Many times the Lord communicates most clearly to the husband through his wife.

The husband and wife should agree on major decisions, because they both will experience the consequences. Even if their choice proves to be disastrous, their relationship remains intact. There are no grounds for an "I told you so" response.

TRAINING CHILDREN

Each generation is responsible for passing on the Gospel and the truths of Scripture, including God's financial principles, to its children. Proverbs 22:6 reads, *"Train up a child in the way he should go, even when he is old he will not depart from it."*

Answer this question: When you left home, how well prepared were you to make financial decisions? Parents and teachers spend 18 to 22 years preparing our youth for occupations, but generally they spend less than a few hours teaching children the value and use of the money they will earn during their careers. To teach biblical principles of handling money, parents should use these three methods: verbal communication, modeling, and practical experience.

VERBAL COMMUNICATION

The Lord charged the Israelites, *"These words, which I am commanding you today, shall be on your heart. You shall teach them diligently to your sons and shall talk of them when you sit in your house and when you walk by the way and when you lie down and when you rise up"* (Deuteronomy 6:6-7). We must verbally instruct our children in the ways of the Lord, but children need more than mere verbal instruction; they also need a good example.

MODELING

Children soak up parental attitudes toward money like a sponge soaks up water. Parents need to be models of how to handle money faithfully. Paul recognized the importance of example when he said, *"Be imitators of me, just as I also am of Christ"* (1 Corinthians 11:1).

A challenging passage for parents is, *"Everyone, after he has been fully trained, will be like his teacher"* (Luke 6:40). Another way of saying this is that we can teach what we believe, but we only reproduce who we are. We must be good models.

When parents encounter challenges, the way they respond in front of their children will demonstrate whether Christ is really Lord in their lives.

PRACTICAL EXPERIENCES

Children need to be given opportunities to apply what they have heard and seen. Learning to handle money should be part of a child's education. Consider several areas where this is possible.

1. Income

As soon as children are ready for school they should begin to receive income to manage. The amount of the income will vary according to such factors as the children's ages, ability to earn, and the financial circumstances of the family. However, the amount of the income is not as important as the responsibility of handling money. At first it is a new experience, and children probably will make many mistakes. Do not hesitate to let the "law of natural consequences" run its course. You are going to be tempted to help your children when they spend all their

The habit of saving should be established as soon as a child receives an income.

income the first day on an unwise purchase. *But do not bail them out!* Their mistakes will be the best teacher.

Parents should establish boundaries and offer advice on how to spend money, but children must have freedom of choice within those boundaries. Excessive restrictions will only reduce the opportunities to learn by experience. The first few pennies and nickels will make a lasting impression.

2. Budgeting

When children start to receive an income, teach them how to budget. Begin with a simple bank consisting of three categories, each labeled separately: "give," "save," and "spend." The child distributes a portion of income into each box. Thus a simple budget is established by using visual control. Even a six-year-old can understand this method, because when there is no more money to spend, the spending box is empty!

When children become teenagers, it is wise to train them to use one of the budgeting software programs that are available. During the budget training, teach your children to become wise consumers. Teach shopping skills, the ability to distinguish needs from wants, and the fine art of waiting on the Lord to provide. Warn them about the powerful influence of advertising and the danger of impulse spending.

3. Saving and investing

The habit of saving should be established as soon as children receive income. It is helpful to open savings accounts in the children's names at this time. As they mature, they should also be exposed to various types of investments: stocks, bonds, real estate, and the like. Teach your children the benefits of compounding interest. If they grasp this concept and become faithful savers, they will enjoy financial stability as adults.

4. Debt

It is also important to teach the cost of money and how difficult it is to get out of debt. A father loaned his son and daughter the money to buy bicycles. He drew up a credit agreement with a schedule for repayment of the loan, including the interest charged. After they went through the long process of paying off the loan, the family celebrated with a "mortgage burning" ceremony at a family picnic. The father said that his children appreciated those bikes more than any of their possessions, and they vowed to avoid debt in the future.

5. Giving

The best time to establish the personal habit of giving is when you are young. It is helpful for children to give a portion of their gifts to a tangible need they can visualize. For example, children understand the impact of their gifts when their contributions are helping to build a church under construction or buying food for a needy family they know.

U.S. Senate Chaplain Richard Halverson gave his son Chris this rich heritage as a child. Chris gave money to support Kim, a Korean orphan who had lost his sight during the Korean War. Chris was taught to feel that Kim was like an adopted brother. One Christmas, Chris bought Kim a harmonica. It was Kim's first personal possession, and he cherished this gift and learned to play it well. Today, Kim is an evangelist and his presentation of the Gospel includes playing the harmonica. By being trained to give as a youth, Chris experienced firsthand the value of meeting people's needs; and, as a result of faithful giving, he saw God change lives.

Any track coach will tell you relay races are won or lost in the passing of the baton from one runner to another. Seldom is the baton dropped once it is firmly in the grasp of a sprinting runner. If it is going to be dropped, it is in the exchange between the runners. As parents we have the responsibility to pass the baton of practical biblical truths to our children. At times during the training it seems as if there is little progress. But be *consistent and persistent!*

INHERITANCE

Parents should attempt to leave a material inheritance to their children. *"A good man leaves an inheritance to his children's children"* (Proverbs 13:22). The inheritance should not be dispensed until the child has been thoroughly trained to be a wise steward. *"An inheritance gained hurriedly at the beginning will not be blessed in the end"* (Proverbs 20:21).

In our opinion you should make provision in your will for distributing an inheritance over several years or until the heir is mature enough to handle the responsibility of money. Select those you trust to supervise the youth until he or she is a capable steward. *"Now I say, as long as the heir is a child, he does not differ at all from a slave although he is owner of everything, but he is under guardians and managers until the date set by the father"* (Galatians 4:1-2).

We recommend a family time each week for dedicating that week's gifts to the Lord.

WILLS

As Isaiah told Hezekiah, *"Thus says the Lord, 'Set your house in order, for you shall die'"* (2 Kings 20:1). Someday, if the Lord tarries, you will die. One of the greatest gifts you can leave your family for that emotional time will be an organized estate and a properly prepared will or trust. If you do not have a current will or trust, please make an appointment this week with an attorney to prepare one.

FINANCIAL HOPE

Crown Financial Ministries offers an Internet driven resource for finding answers to financial questions. It is clear that finances touch every life and, no matter where someone is in his or her personal financial journey, Crown Financial Ministries can assist in finding the guidance desired. Working with a Money Map Coach is a vital move to getting finances in order. Along with the Money Map Coach, Financial Hope may be able to help. The following information will give you an idea of what Financial Hope has to offer.

What financial challenges do you face today? What information are you looking for?

- Do you want to establish a spending plan or make sure your plan is on track?
- Do you desire relief from worry and tension about overdue bills?
- Do you want the absolute assurance that God is in control of your finances?
- Do you have questions about your financial future, retirement, or investing?

If any of these questions relates to you, then Financial Hope can help! Many people want to know what they can do to break out of the debt cycle. How much debt/credit can someone or a family practically handle? Is there a balance? Anyone can become debt free and stay that way, given the desire, discipline, and time. With an abundance of learning opportunities ranging from one-to-one coaching to topical seminars, from small group studies to self-help resource books, and even credit counseling, Crown has resources to meet your needs.

The Web address is www.financialhope.com.

IS THE JOURNEY OVER? WHAT NOW?

You have successfully completed the *Journey to Financial Freedom Manual*. Congratulations! We pray that it was very helpful to you financially and spiritually. We want to extend an invitation to you to continue to learn more about God's financial principles and to help reach others through Crown Financial Ministries.

For updates and spiritual encouragement you will want to sign up for Crown's weekly e-mail and to receive our monthly newsletter, *Money Matters* by e-mail. The *Money Matters* newsletter is also available in print. You also may want to join a Crown Small Group Study or attend a seminar. For information on these and all the other products, training, and services offered by Crown Financial Ministries, call 1-800-722-1976 anytime from 8:30 A.M. until 4:30 P.M. EST or visit us on the Web at www.crown.org.

May God bless you as you honor Him. Please let us know if we can be of any future assistance to you.

BUDGET
FORMS

MONTHLY INCOME AND EXPENSES

GROSS INCOME PER MONTH _____

    Salary _____

    Interest _____

    Dividends _____

    Other (_____) _____

    Other (_____) _____

LESS:

1. **Tithe** _____

2. **Tax** (Est. - Incl. Fed., State, FICA) _____

    NET SPENDABLE INCOME _____

3. **Housing** _____

    Mortgage (rent) _____

    Insurance _____

    Taxes _____

    Electricity _____

    Gas _____

    Water _____

    Sanitation _____

    Telephone _____

    Maintenance _____

    Other (_____) _____

    Other (_____) _____

4. **Food** _____

5. **Automobile(s)** _____

    Payments _____

    Gas and Oil _____

    Insurance _____

    License/Taxes _____

    Maint./Repair/Replace _____

6. **Insurance** _____

    Life _____

    Medical _____

    Other (_____) _____

7. **Debts** _____

    Credit Card _____

    Loans and Notes _____

    Other (_____) _____

    Other (_____) _____

8. **Enter./Recreation** _____

    Eating Out _____

    Baby Sitters _____

    Activities/Trips _____

    Vacation _____

    Other (_____) _____

    Other (_____) _____

9. **Clothing** _____

10. **Savings** _____

11. **Medical Expenses** _____

    Doctor _____

    Dentist _____

    Credit Card _____

    Other (_____) _____

12. **Miscellaneous** _____

    Toiletry, cosmetics _____

    Beauty, barber _____

    Laundry, cleaning _____

    Allowances, lunches _____

    Subscriptions _____

    Gifts (incl. Christmas) _____

    Cash _____

    Cable/Internet _____

    Other (_____) _____

    Other (_____) _____

13. **Investments** _____

14. **School/Child Care** _____

    Tuition _____

    Materials _____

    Transportation _____

    Day Care _____

    Other (_____) _____

    TOTAL EXPENSES _____

INCOME VERSUS EXPENSES

    Net Spendable Income _____

    Less Expenses _____

15. **Unallocated Surplus Income**[1]

[1] This category is used when surplus income is received. This would be kept in the checking account to be used within a few weeks; otherwise, it should be transferred to an allocated category.

Crown Financial Ministries 2/03

LIST OF DEBTS

as of _____

To Whom Owed	Contact Name Phone Number	Pay Off	Payments Left	Monthly Payment	Date Due	Interest Rate

Crown Financial Ministries 2/03

FINANCIAL STATEMENT

as of _____

ASSETS
Liquid Assets[1]

_____ $ _____

_____

_____

_____

_____

Total Liquid Assets $ _____

Invested Assets[2]

_____ $ _____

_____

_____

_____

_____

Total Invested $ _____

Use Assets[3]

_____ $ _____

_____

_____

_____

_____

Total Use Assets $ _____

TOTAL ASSETS $ _____

LIABILITIES[4]

_____ $ _____

_____

_____

_____

_____

TOTAL LIABILITIES $ _____

NET WORTH $ _____
(Assets-Liabilities)

**TOTAL LIABILITIES
AND NET WORTH** $ _____

[1] Cash, Savings Accounts, Checking Accounts
[2] IRAs, TSAs, 401(K)s, Investment, Real Estate, CDs, Antiques presented at fair market value.
[3] Residence, Autos, Personal Belongings presented at fair market value.
[4] Outstanding Real Estate Loans, Credit Cards, Auto Loans, Personal Loans.

Crown Financial Ministries 2/03

INCOME ALLOCATION

INCOME		INCOME SOURCE/PAY PERIOD			
BUDGET CATEGORY	**MONTHLY ALLOCATION**				
1. Tithe					
2. Tax					
3. Housing					
4. Food					
5. Auto					
6. Insurance					
7. Debts					
8. Entertainment/ Recreation					
9. Clothing					
10. Savings					
11. Medical/Dental					
12. Miscellaneous					
13. School/Child Care					
14. Investments					
15. Unallocated Surplus Income					

Crown Financial Ministries 2/03

INDIVIDUAL ACCOUNT PAGE

_____ $_____ $_____
ACCOUNT CATEGORY   ALLOCATION   ALLOCATION

DATE	TRANSACTION	DEPOSIT	WITHDRAW	BALANCE

Crown Financial Ministries 2/03

Financial Goals for the _____ family

Category	Specific Goal	Time Frame	Goal Successfully Met
Savings	We will save $5 a week to place toward a lamp replacement	6 weeks	1-June
Debt Retirement	We will reduce our consumer debt by $100 per month until it is gone	Monthly	1/31, 2/29, 3/31, 4/31
Offering	We will give an additional $25 per month to the church for missionary work	Ongoing as God provides	1/31, 2/29,

Personal and Spiritual Goals for the _____ family

Category	Specific Goal	Time Frame	Goal Successfully Met
Personal Goals			
Spiritual Goals			

Crown Financial Ministries 2/03

Month	Year	Monthly Budget						

Monthly Budget

Category	INCOME	TITHE/GIVING	TAXES	HOUSING	FOOD	TRANSPORTATION	INSURANCE
BUDGETED AMOUNT	$	$	$	$	$	$	$
Date							
1							
2							
3							
4							
5							
6							
7							
8							
9							
10							
11							
12							
13							
14							
15							
This month SUBTOTAL	$	$	$	$	$	$	$
16							
17							
18							
19							
20							
21							
22							
23							
24							
25							
26							
27							
28							
29							
30							
31							
This month TOTAL	$	$	$	$	$	$	$
This month SURPLUS/DEFICIT	$	$	$	$	$	$	$
Year to Date BUDGET	$	$	$	$	$	$	$
Year to Date TOTAL	$	$	$	$	$	$	$
Year to Date SURPLUS/DEFICIT	$	$	$	$	$	$	$

BUDGET SUMMARY

This Month		Previous Month/Year to Date		Year to Date
Total Income $ _____		Total Income $ _____		Total Income $ _____
Minus Total Expenses $ _____	**+**	Minus Total Expenses $ _____	**=**	Minus Total Expenses $ _____
Equals Surplus/Deficit $ _____		Equals Surplus/Deficit $ _____		Equals Surplus/Deficit $ _____

Monthly Budget

Category	DEBTS	ENT./REC.	CLOTHING	SAVINGS	MEDICAL	MISCELLANEOUS	INVESTMENTS	SCHOOL/DAYCARE
BUDGETED AMOUNT	$	$	$	$	$	$	$	$
Date								
1								
2								
3								
4								
5								
6								
7								
8								
9								
10								
11								
12								
13								
14								
15								
This month SUBTOTAL	$	$	$	$	$	$	$	$
16								
17								
18								
19								
20								
21								
22								
23								
24								
25								
26								
27								
28								
29								
30								
31								
This month TOTAL	$	$	$	$	$	$	$	$
This month SURPLUS/DEFICIT	$	$	$	$	$	$	$	$
Year to Date BUDGET	$	$	$	$	$	$	$	$
Year to Date TOTAL	$	$	$	$	$	$	$	$
Year to Date SURPLUS/DEFICIT	$	$	$	$	$	$	$	$

VARIABLE EXPENSE PLANNING

1. VACATION $_____ ÷ 12 = $_____

2. DENTIST $_____ ÷ 12 = $_____

3. DOCTOR $_____ ÷ 12 = $_____

4. AUTOMOBILE $_____ ÷ 12 = $_____

5. ANNUAL INSURANCE $_____ ÷ 12 = $_____

(Life) ($_____ ÷ 12 = $_____)

(Health) ($_____ ÷ 12 = $_____)

(Auto) ($_____ ÷ 12 = $_____)

(Home) ($_____ ÷ 12 = $_____)

6. CLOTHING $_____ ÷ 12 = $_____

7. INVESTMENTS $_____ ÷ 12 = $_____

8. GIFTS $_____ ÷ 12 = $_____

9. _____ $_____ ÷ 12 = $_____

10. _____ $_____ ÷ 12 = $_____

11. _____ $_____ ÷ 12 = $_____

12. _____ $_____ ÷ 12 = $_____

Plan for those expenses that are not paid on a regular monthly basis by estimating the yearly cost and determining the monthly amount neeeded to be set aside for that expense. A helpful formula is to allow the previous year's expense and add 5 percent.

Crown Financial Ministries 12/04

INVOLVEMENT AND SUGGESTIONS

Date:_____

We want to seek your counsel. The suggestions of past coaching participants have significantly improved the coaching process. We also want to invite you to join with us in helping to train others to handle money biblically. To mail us this form postage free, please fold according to the guides on the next page, seal (tape), and mail.

Please Print

YOUR NAME   ☐ MR   ☐ MRS   ☐ MS   ☐ MISS   ☐ DR   ☐ REV

HOME ADDRESS

CITY   ST/PROV   ZIP/POSTAL CODE

COUNTRY

HOME PHONE   WORK PHONE

E-MAIL ADDRESS

NAME OF MONEY MAP COACH

NEWSLETTER AND E-MAIL

We send a weekly e-mail message and monthly newsletter sharing God's principles and communicating what the Lord is doing in CROWN FINANCIAL MINISTRIES. Please indicate below if you would like to receive these.

☐ Yes, I would like to like to receive CROWN'S weekly e-mail message.
☐ Yes, I would like to receive the monthly *Money Matters* newsletter.
☐ Yes, I would like to receive the monthly *Money Matters* newsletter by E-mail.

INVOLVEMENT

PRAY

☐ Yes, I would like to pray regularly for the Lord to expand CROWN and change lives through this ministry.

SERVE

Please send me information on:
☐ Becoming trained as a small group leader.
☐ Becoming trained as a Money Map Coach.
☐ Serving with CROWN in my church.

SUPPORT

☐ Enclosed is a contribution to CROWN in the amount of $_____.
☐ I want to become a CROWN Outreach Partner and a regular supporter of CROWN. Enclosed is my first contribution in the amount of $_____.

BUSINESS REPLY MAIL
FIRST-CLASS MAIL   PERMIT NO 95   GAINESVILLE GA

POSTAGE WILL BE PAID BY ADDRESSEE

Crown Financial Ministries
PO Box 100
Gainesville GA 30503-9931

Please tri-fold and seal. Do not staple.

1. What was the most valuable part of the study? Please be specific.

2. Do you have any suggestions for improving any areas?

3. Describe any insights that would help others.

We would be very appreciative if you would share what the Lord has done in your life through this study or if you have any practical hints that would be especially helpful for other people.

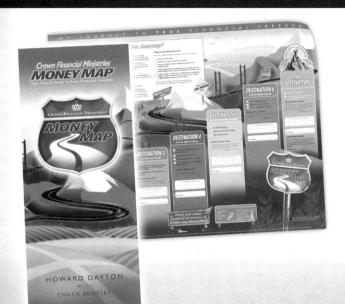

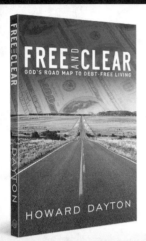